GORDON LEWIN

Twenty-two Unaccompanied Pieces for Saxophone

☆ ☆ ☆ ☆ ☆ ☆ ☆ ☆ ☆ ☆ ☆ ☆ ☆ ☆ ☆ ☆

THE ASSOCIATED BOARD OF
THE ROYAL SCHOOLS OF MUSIC

GAVOTTE
from French Suite No.5

Edited by Gordon Lewin

J. S. BACH

A B 1858

SARABANDE

Edited by Gordon Lewin

TARTINI
(1692-1770)

THE GOLDEN VANITY

Arranged by Gordon Lewin

Based on
ENGLISH FOLK TUNE

ROSLIN CASTLE

Arranged by Gordon Lewin

Based on
SCOTS AIR

Lamentoso

CHOUCONNE

Arranged by Gordon Lewin

Based on
TRAD. CARIBBEAN SONG

★ ♩ — start note slightly flat and lip up to true pitch

INTRODUCTION AND THEME

from 'Witches' Dance'

Edited by Gordon Lewin

PAGANINI, Op. 8 Posth.

A TEAR

Edited by Gordon Lewin

MOUSSORGSKY

NANA AND EL PAÑO

Arranged by Gordon Lewin

ANDALUCIAN FOLK SONGS

THE JOLLY HUNTSMAN

Edited by Gordon Lewin

G. MERKEL
(1827-1885)

COAST ROAD

GORDON LEWIN

SHALOM ALECHUM

(Peace unto you)

Arranged by Gordon Lewin

TRAD. ISRAELI SONG

AB 1858

GAVOTTE

Edited by Gordon Lewin

TELEMANN

PRETTY BRIDE

Arranged by Gordon Lewin

Based on
TWO ISRAELI FOLK SONGS

BOURREE

Edited by Gordon Lewin

HANDEL, Op.1 No.5

Allegretto

GOLDEN SANDS

GORDON LEWIN

PASSEPIED

Edited by Gordon Lewin

DALL'ABACO
(1675-1742)

HAVU EZ LATAISH

Arranged by Gordon Lewin

from a 19th-century
ISRAELI OPERETTA

HAWK GETS BIRD

GORDON LEWIN

★ ♩—start note slightly flat and lip up to true pitch

A VINTAGE DANCE

Edited by Gordon Lewin

GUSTAV LANGE
(1830-1889)

MASTER ERSKINE'S HORNPIPE

Arranged by Gordon Lewin

Based on
TRAD. SCOTTISH HORNPIPE
(1853)

EL VITO

Arranged by Gordon Lewin

Based on
ANDALUCIAN FOLK SONG

ARIA
from 'The Barber of Seville'

Edited by Gordon Lewin

ROSSINI

Moderato

Printed in England by Caligraving Limited Thetford Norfolk

AB 1815

2:98